GRAN'S OLD-FASH
WRINKLES

*Gran – Elizabeth Ann Manley – on the day she
became engaged, 21 April 1898*

GRAN'S OLD-FASHIONED REMEDIES, WRINKLES AND RECIPES

by Jean Penny

(author of *Gran's Old-Fashioned Gardening Gems*)

EX LIBRIS PRESS

Original edition published by New Horizon, 1980
Expanded and revised edition first published 1988
Reprinted 1989, 1990
New edition 1992
Reprinted 1993 and 1995

EX LIBRIS PRESS
1 The Shambles
Bradford on Avon
Wiltshire

Typeset in 10 point Century Schoolbook
Design and Typesetting by Ex Libris Press
Cover by 46 Design, Bradford on Avon

Cover printed by Shires Press, Trowbridge
Printed and bound in Great Britain
by Cromwell Press, Broughton Gifford, Wiltshire

ISBN 0 948578 36 X

*To Elizabeth Ann Manley,
27 October 1878 - 13 April 1979
Most loving Grandmother*

Note: All the old engravings reproduced in these pages are
taken from an edition of Mary Russell Mitford's *Our Village*,
published by Sampson Low in 1882.

Preface

This book presents a slice of social history for it offers traditional remedies and cures used in days prior to the world we live in today.

My mother gave me all the information which had been handed down through generations from my great-grandmother who was a cook in a private girls school in Taunton in the last century and my grandmother Elizabeth Anne Manley to whom this book is dedicated.

My great-grandmother lived to over 90 and my grandmother, who lived to be over 100, thought nothing of walking five miles to visit friends and relatives and throughout her long lifetime she lived in and ran her own home. Dainty, spirited and with a tremendous sense of humour she could recall not only events that had happened when she was young but more recent events just as clearly.

The remedies, tips and recipes reflect a time when necessity was the mother of invention and little or nothing was wasted. They are as useful today as they were long ago. I trust you will find them of service.

Jean Penny
Somerset, 1988

Gran's daughter — the author's mother — in 1905,
at the age of three

CONTENTS

REMEDIES

ALCOHOL 17
ARTHRITIS 17
BLOOD PURIFIER 17
BRONCHITIS 18
BRUISES AND BURNS 18
CHAPPED HANDS AND CHILBLAINS 19
COLD — a one night cure 19
   To cure 19
CONSTIPATION 20
CORNS 20
SOFT CORNS 20
COUGH, SORE THROAT 20
CRAMP 21
DIARRHOEA 21
DIGESTION 22
EYES 22
FEET — To soothe 22
   Pinch on feet and fingers 22
FINGER — splinter in 23
HAIR — Baldness 23
   Falling Hair 23
   Grey Hair 23
HAY FEVER 24
HEADACHES 24
LUMBAGO 24
MOUTH ULCERS 25
NAIL — ingrowing 25
SORE LIPS 25
SPOTS AND BOILS 25

TEETH Plaque   26
TENDER FEET   26
VOICE — Loss of   26
MEDICINE CUPBOARD   26
TURPENTINE   26

WRINKLES

AIR — To purify   27
APPLES — An easy way to peel them   27
APRICOTS — Tinned   27
BABIES   27
BATH STAINS   27
BOOK LEAVES   27
BRAN — For cleaning purposes   28
BRASSES — Cleaning   28
BREAD   29
BURNING OIL — To extinguish   29
CAKE MAKING AND PUDDINGS — Dredging   29
    Prevention of burning   29
    Pudding test   30
CANDLES   30
CARPETS — laying   30
    Stair carpet   30
CHIMNEYS   30
CHINA — Care of   31
    Discoloured   31
    To mend   31
CLOTHES LINES   31
COPPER KETTLE   31
CUT GLASS   31
CUTLERY — Fish odour   32
    To clean rusty knives   32
    Stained knife handles   32
DINING TABLE   32
DISINFECTANT   32
EGGS   33

Contents

ENAMEL BATH TUBS 33
FINGER MARKS ON DOORS 33
FLOOR STAIN 33
FRUIT — Sour 33
   Raspberries, to keep 33
FURNITURE DUST 34
GLASS 34
GLASSES (SPECTACLES) 34
HOT GREASE SPILLAGE 34
JAM — To keep 34
LAMP LIGHT — To improve 35
LINOLEUM — To clean 35
LINOLEUM CREAM 35
MACHINE GREASE 35
MATTING 35
MEAT — Tough 36
MENUS 37
MICE 37
MILK To prevent boiling over 37
   To prevent burning 37
   Burnt and scorched milk 37
   To preserve 37
   To prevent going sour 37
MIRRORS 37
MOTHS 38
MUD STAINS 38
MUSTARD 38
ONIONS 39
PAPERED WALLS — Marks and stains 39
PEARS — Preservation of 39
PICKLES 39
PIPE LEAKING — To stop a gas or water leak 39
PLANTS — To water when absent 39
POLISH 40
   Boot 40
   Shoe polish 40
   Piano 40
POTATOES — Frosted 40

PRESERVES   40
RUSTY KEYS AND LOCKS   41
SALT   41
SARDINES   41
SCREW — To remove rusty screw   41
SOAP SCRAPS   41
STAINS   41
  Fruit   41
  Paint on glass   41
  Green on brick tiles or steps   41
STOVE BLACKING   42
  To prevent turning brown   42
TENNIS BALLS   42
TILED FLOOR   42
VEGETABLES   42
WAX POLISH   43
WINDOWS — Cleaning panes   43
WOODEN TOP TABLES   43

WRINKLES FOR CLOTHES AND TOILET CARE

ARTIFICIAL FLOWERS   45
ASPARAGUS WATER   45
BLACK CASHMERE — To clean   45
BLACK LACE — Renovating   45
BLOUSE — To secure inside skirt   46
BLOUSES — Net   46
  How to wash   46
BOOTS — Tight   47
BOOT AND SHOE LEATHER — Care of   47
BROWN NECK — To whiten   48
  Oatmeal Poultice   48
BUTTONHOLES   48

Contents

COMPLEXION   48
  Lotion   48
  Care of   48
  To whiten the skin   48
CLOTHES — To prevent blue streaking   49
CORSET STEELS   49
ELDERFLOWER WATER   49
FURS   50
GREASE SPOTS   50
GREASY SKIN   50
HAIR — Fair   51
HAIR — Wavy   51
HANDS — To whiten   52
CROWN OF A HAT   52
LACE — To starch old lace   52
NAILS — To prevent split   53
PAPER PATTERNS — Care of   53
RELINING A COAT   53
RIBBONS (HAIR RIBBONS)   53
RIBBONS — To stiffen   54
SACHETS — Perfumed   54
SATIN SHOES — To clean   54
SERGE SKIRT — Navy blue or black   55
SILK (TUSSORE) RENOVATION   55
TO RENOVATE A SHABBY SILK UMBRELLA   55
SILK   55
  To brush
  Washing white or cream silk   55
WHITE SILK   56
SPONGE   56
  Slimy   56
  Hard sponge — to soften   56
STOCKINGS   57
SUNSHADE, LINEN — To clean   57
SUNSHADE — To wash   57
TOOTH POWDER   57
TORTOISE-SHELL ORNAMENTS, COMBS, ETC.   57

VEILS   58
   Care of   58
   Sight impaired by   58
VELVET   59
VELVETEEN   59
WATER — To soften   60
WATER SOFTENER for my lady's toilet   60
WHITE WOOLLEN SHAWLS — To clean   60
WRINKLED HANDS   61

RECIPES

SAVOURY

BEAN FEAST   63
BOILED LEG OF LAMB   63
BRUSSELS SPROUT PUREE   64
CABBAGE BALLS   64
CHEESE CUSTARD   64
COD CAPERS   65
COLLARED HEAD   66
CURRY BALLS   66
FISH CREAM   67
FLEMISH CARROTS   67
MOCK BOILED CHICKEN   68
MOCK DUCK   68
MOCK JUGGED HARE   69
OATMEAL BLANMANGE   69
PICKLED NASTURTIUMS   69
RICE SAVOURY   70
ROAST PHEASANT   70
SHEEP'S HEART   70
SKATE AND CAPER SAUCE   71
SWEETBREADS   71
VEGETARIAN CUTLETS   72

PUDDINGS AND SWEETS

APPLE CREAM   73
BANANA CREAM   73
BANANA CROQUETTES   74
BURNT CREAM   74
BUTTERCUP JELLY   75
CALVES' FOOT LEMON PUDDING   75
CANADIAN BLANCMANGE   76
CANARY PUDDING   76
CHESTNUT SURPRISE   76
CHOCOLATE CUSTARD   77
CRANBERRY JELLY   77
DEANERY PUDDING   78
DUCHESS PUDDING   78
DUTCH PUDDING   79
FLUMMERY   79
FRUIT SALAD   79
IMPERIAL PUDDING   80
MARBLE JELLY   81
PEACH SPONGE   81
QUINCE JELLY   82
RED APPLE JELLY   82
ROWAN JELLY   82
VANILLA SOUFFLE   83
YORK CREAM   83
YORK TARTLETS   84

CAKES

BROWNEY BROWNEY CAKE   85
SEMOLINA CAKE   85
SUGAR COOKIES   85

SWEETS AND CANDIES

FUDGE   86
POPCORN   86

FOR INVALIDS AND CONVALESCENTS

ALBUMEN WATER   87
ALMOND RESTORATIVE   87
ARROWROOT JELLY   87
CALF'S FOOT JELLY   88
COW HEEL JELLY   89
CREAM JELLY   89
EGG JELLY   89
INVALID PUDDING   90
MILK TEA   90
RAW BEEF TEA   90

BISCUITS

KRINGLES   91
JUMBLES   91
SODA BISCUITS   91

BEVERAGES

CANADIAN OATMEAL WATER   92
ELDERFLOWER CHAMPAGNE   92
GINGER POP   92
HEALTH LEMONADE   93
LEMON BARLEY WATER   93
LEMON POWDER   93
WINTER DRINK   94

INCIDENTALS

BOTTLED LEMON JUICE   94
FRUIT SALAD DRESSING   94
IMITATION CREAM   95

HEALTH FOR BABIES AND CHILDREN

WALKING   95
TABLE MANNERS   95
EARLY TRAINING IN SLEEPING HABITS   95

REMEDIES

ALCOHOL
Alcohol is harmful to the complexion; fattening; and death can result from alcoholic poisoning.

Alcohol is rapidly absorbed into the bloodstream and induces a feeling of warmth and well-being. It impairs control of the finer perceptions, both of a mental and muscular nature.

To avoid a hangover drink two large glasses of water before retiring to bed. Never drink on an empty stomach.

Strong alcohol, if used locally, can produce irritation and damage BUT it may be used for hardening the skin and also as an antiseptic because it kills bacteria.

Make sure it doesn't kill you.

ARTHRITIS
To alleviate arthritis place 24 chillies in a small (miniature) bottle of whisky. Leave to steep for 24 hours. Then take one teaspoonful each day.

NB This remedy is very unpleasant and hot to take.

Drinking plenty of water is considered to be beneficial to those suffering from arthritis.

BLOOD PURIFIER
Take two ounces of Epsom salts, half an ounce of milk of sulphur, an ounce and a half of powdered ginger, half an ounce of cream of tartar, the juice of a lemon and the thin rind.

Pour two quarts of boiling water over all the ingredients. Leave for 12 hours, then strain and bottle.

Dosage: A wineglassful two or three times a day for an adult.

A Granny saying — 'Remember a pain is Nature's way of telling you something is wrong ... see to it.'

BRONCHITIS

Wrap the patient in warm garments and keep him in a warm room with an even temperature of 60 degrees, not allowing it to drop during the night. Rub the chest and back with a little warm camphorated oil mixed with equal parts of olive oil.

After the oil has been rubbed in put a thin layer of cotton-wool on the chest and the back. If the bronchitis shows no sign of yielding to this treatment, a doctor should be sent for immediately.

BRUISES AND BURNS

Always keep a bottle of olive oil in the house in case of accidents.

Should a child fall and bump its head, rub the place at once, but gently with plenty of olive oil. This should fetch the bruise out. Keep the child quiet for a time.

For a burn or scald, smother the place with olive oil, then with flour. Bind it up with a soft, clean white rag to keep the air from getting to the burn.

In all serious cases send for the doctor immediatly.

CHAPPED HANDS, CHILBLAINS

'Prevention is better than cure', so they say. This may be ensured by simply crushing some ordinary white starch and keeping it in a box close at hand. Then after washing your hands in the usual way, partially dry them and then rub some of the powdered starch all over them. The soothing and healing effect of this has to be tried to be realised and it has the advantage of being a quick and clean process.

To prevent chilblains wear warm and easy footwear. Keep the circulation active in the feet. If they feel cold on coming from the outside air, place them in hot water and rub with a warm towel.

For a commencing chilblain camphorated oil can be of service.

For a tender chilblain one of the best remedies is belladonna ointment.

A broken chilblain should always be treated as an open wound. Rest, warmth and dressing of lint covered with freshly made oxide-of-zinc ointment will set matters right.

COLD — A one night cure

A cold either in the head or the chest can nearly always be stopped and cured in one night if taken in time.

Undress, put on a flannel nightgown and wrap a blanket around yourself. Then sit for several hours with your feet and ankles in a foot bath of mustard and water as hot as you can bear it, adding more water as necessary, as time goes by.

Meanwhile, sip a pint of hot strong lemonade; then dry your feet quickly and get into bed, still with the blanket wrapped around you, for the touch of cold sheets could make you shiver and undo all the good of the hot bath and the drink.

The cold will probably be gone in the morning but you should feed up well on nourishing food.

TO CURE A COLD

Take two large Spanish onions, divide into small pieces and put into a saucepan with a saltspoonful of salt, three ounces of butter and a pint of cold water. Simmer until tender, then pour into a hot basin, sprinkle with pepper and eat as hot as possible just before going to a warm bed.

CONSTIPATION

This condition may be relieved by taking a glass of warm water the last thing at night and first thing in the morning.

Sufferers should eat plenty of stewed fruit, such as figs, etc., green vegetables and salads with plenty of oil.

CORNS

Make a poultice by soaking breadcrumbs well in vinegar. Tie it on the corn overnight, and after taking it off next morning, squeeze a drop or two of lemon juice on the corn and put on a corn plaster, or tie the toe up with a bit of fine, clean rag.

You may have to poultice it for several nights before it is cured. OR Wash the root of a dandelion; then rub the corn with the sap. *Soft Corns:* To cure a painful soft corn between the toes, sprinkle it with a little powdered alum night and morning. OR soak a small ivy leaf in vinegar for a day, then bind the leaf gently round the corn. Change it every morning until cured. OR remove all parts possible around the corn, and then put round it or between the toes, cotton wool soaked in olive oil.

COUGH, SORE THROAT

A useful and a soothing cough mixture for a dry tickling cough can be made up as follows:

Mix one ounce of syrup of squills with one tablespoon each of glycerine and honey.

Take one teaspoonful stirred into two teaspoonsful of water at night, whenever troublesome.

Another useful remedy for sore throats and coughs is linseed tea:

Linseed Tea: Take two heaped tablespoonsful of whole linseed, tie loosely in a clean piece of muslin, put into a saucepan with one pint of cold water. Bring quickly to the boil, draw to the side of the fire, and simmer slowly for four hours, keeping the water up to one pint. Then pour into a jug, add the strained juice of a large lemon and a tablespoonful of sugar. Stir well, and take a wine-glassful when cough is troublesome. This is very successful for young and old.

Linseed Poultice: It may not be generally known that a little cayenne pepper sprinkled on a linseed poultice can be used instead of mustard. It does not blister, but keeps the poultice warm and comfortable much longer. If for any reason a poultice of any sort is ordered to be put next to the skin with no cloth or muslin interfering, it will be better to first grease the skin with a little vaseline or sweet oil to prevent sticking.

OR for A Sore Throat: Put home-cured, salty fat bacon around your throat. Secure it with a face cloth or scarf; rub gooses grease on your chest, and then to bed.

CRAMP

This comes from over-fatigue and is caused by muscle contraction. If in the arms and legs, rub with a hot flannel and stretch the limbs. If it attacks the stomach a very little hot water and ginger does good. The sufferer should get into a warm bed if the pain endures, and medical opinion and advice should be taken

To prevent cramp during the night sleep with several bottle corks in the bedding.

During periods of cramp hot linseed poultices containing mustard should be applied and the feet should be kept warm.

DIARRHOEA

Take rice milk made in the following way: allow one ounce of well washed rice to a pint of new milk. Let it simmer until it is soft enough to rub through a sieve. Turn it into a saucepan with a bit of cinnamon and a little loaf sugar. Make it hot, and serve with a crisp unsweetened biscuit.

More milk can be added if the mixture is too thick.

DIGESTION

For weak digestion. Stand a quart of new milk in a cool larder fro six hours. Skim off seven tablespoonsful and put it aside. Then skim off half a pint and use it for the house; with the remaining 26 ounces make whey in the following manner.

Pour the milk into a basin and take enough rennet to curdle. Rennet tablets may be used ... full directions are usually given on each tablet. Take sixteen ounces of whey, add one teaspoonful of milk and sugar and heat, but do not boil. Allow to cool. Add an ounce of lime water and the cream you skimmed off the top of the milk.

Warm the mixture and give it to the patient as required.

EYES

Workers should rest their eyes frequently both by day and night by just shading them with the hand for a minute at a time, about every half an hour. This is really a wonderful preservative.

If the eyes feel gritty and tired, bathe them frequently with warm weak boracic lotion or warm salt and water or weak tepid tea. And a tea leaf poultice tied on at night is very soothing and strengthening.

FEET — To soothe

If your feet get swollen and tender in warm weather, soak them every night in hot salt and water, and after drying them,sponge them with vinegar. Toilet vinegar is nicest, but ordinary vinegar serves the same purpose.

To prevent swelling and chilblains ... get alittle bottle of rectified spirits of wine, and dissolve a teaspoonful of rough salt in it. Sponge the feet with this every night and then rub them vigorously with the palm of the hand. Whisky or gin will serve the same purpose ... four tablespoonsful of spirit to one tablespoonful of salt.

Pinch on feet or fingers

Place feet or fingers (whichever were pinched) at once into hot water. This will restore circulation and ease the pain.

If you should happen to squeeze the top of your finger, hold it in warm water for a few minutes. This causes the nail to expand and soften, and the blood beneath has more room to flow, so the pain is lessened.

FINGER — Splinter in

To remove a splinter nearly fill a wide-mouthed bottle with hot water, then hold the injured part over this and hold it down lightly. The suction will act as a poultice and draw the flesh down, when the splinter should come out quite easily.

HAIR — baldness

Bathe the bald spot every morning with water as hot as the scalp can bear. In less than two months a new growth of hair should appear.

Falling hair

A good tonic should be applied to the roots every night. This could be castor oil or olive oil.

Grey Hair

If prematurely grey, the following mixture rubbed thoroughly in to the scalp every night should restore the hair to its proper colour: Tincture of jacorandi, one ounce; hydrochlorate of pilocarpine, six grains; spirit of rosemary, six drachms; pure glycerine, two drachms; rose or elderflower water, six ounces.

You should ask a chemist to make up the preparation.

Olive oil, castor oil and coconut oil are also good for the hair if used regularly.

HAY FEVER

The symptoms of hay fever being sneezing, usually a cold in the head, dryness of the throat and nasal passages with what is best described as an unpleasant heated sensation. It is best relieved by the nasal passages being thoroughly sprayed with an antiseptic cleansing lotion.

HEADACHES

The juice of half a lemon in a cup of black coffee without sugar or milk seldom fails to cure a headache or if taken in time, to prevent one from developing.

LUMBAGO

Although a mustard leaf or plaster is one of the quickest ways of relieving a stiff neck or an attack of lumbago, or a cold in the chest, it is very painful and can leave the skin red and sore for days afterwards. But there is a way of applying mustard so that you can get all the benefit without the soreness. Put the mustard in a cup and mix it to a fairly stiff paste with a little ordinary salad oil. Spread the mixture on one half of a piece of white flannel, fold over the other half and tack it around the edge with needle and thread. The size of the poultice must of course depend on where it is to be worn. For a stiff neck or sore throat it should be long and narrow; for the chest a five inch square; or if it is meant to relieve a chill on the kidneys or lumbago it should be about eight inches long by four deep, and must be kept in place by a bandage or body belt. A piece of oil silk should be worn over it to prevent the yellow mustard oil staining one's clothing and the poultice can be worn for days, if necessary.

> *A Granny saying:*
> *'Ne'er cast a clout, 'til May is out'.*
> *A Granfy saying:*
> *'May oo?'*
> *A granny saying:*
> *' 'Tis bad luck to bring lilac or may into the house.'*
> *A Granfy saying:*
> *'May oo?'*

MOUTH ULCERS
Bitter alum placed on the ulcers will facilitate a cure.

NAIL — ingrowing
A very simple way to remove an ingrowing toe-nail is to get a small piece of wool or wadding to commence with, and press under the ingrowing nail, and add a small piece more daily, and continue walking about. This is most important as the walking presses the nail from the flesh gently; and in a few days the nail will be completely separate from the flesh, and can be cut off without pain or inconvenience.

SORE LIPS
A fairly quick way of dispensing with those disagreable little blisters that sometimes form on the lips as the result of a cold is to touch them with a drop of methylated spirits two or three times a day. Or, if the blister is broken, and forms a sore, touch it with a little powdered alum (this will sting at first) and then apply the lip salve.

SPOTS AND BOILS
Soothe spots and boils with warm milk. Draw out the impurities with a concoction made of carbolic soap mixed with sugar.

TEETH — Plaque
Eating strawberries was considered to be good for your teeth. Now it is alleged to help defeat plaque.

TENDER FEET
Tired tender feet should be soaked every night in hot water with salt. Dry sponge with vinegar.

VOICE — Loss of
A simple remedy for loss of voice is made in the following way: take the white of an egg, beat it and add the juice of one lemon and sufficient castor sugar to sweeten it.

A teaspoonful of this mixture should be taken at short intervals.

MEDICINE CUPBOARD
Every household should have a medicine cupboard. It should be fitted with a good lock and key. Every drug and preparation should be labelled and have on it directions as to how to use it.

A few items which should be found in the medicine cupboard are: castor oil, ipecacuanha wine, carron oil for burns. Lint, a roll or two of bandages, a piece of oil silk, linseed, zinc ointment, a clinical thermometer, vaseline, cotton wool, oil of cloves for tooth-ache, senna pods, sal volatile for shocks and faintness, turpentine, flexible collodion for cuts and scratches, quinine, scissors and a medical glass.

TURPENTINE
Turpentine is a splendid remedy for burns and if mixed with a little flour to form a paste, makes a good cure for a corn.

Rheumatic patients derive much benefit from being rubbed with turpentine before a good fire; it makes a splendid liniment for the throat. It is also a sure help in fits and convulsions.

When washing clothes worn by a person who has had an infectious disease, add a little to the water first; a tablespoonful put into the copper on washing day makes the clothes beautifully white.

NB Turpentine is for external use only. And it is inflammable.

WRINKLES

AIR — To purify
A few drops of oil of lavender poured into a glass of very hot water will purify the air of a sick room and will also instantly remove cooking odours from a room.

It is also most refreshing in a sick room.

Burn a little coffee on a shovel and carry it through a room where cigars have been smoked and it will remove the smell.

APPLES — An easy way to peel them
Pour scalding water over the apples, and then the skins can be easily slipped off, saving labour and waste.

APRICOTS — Tinned
When using tinned apricots from which , as a rule, the kernels have been removed, a few drops of almond flavouring will be found to improve them greatly.

BABIES
Babies respond to loving and fondling and talking. They learn to talk by listening.

BATH STAINS
A solution of soda and water applied with a broom should remove the brown streaks on enamel baths made by sediments in the dripping water.

BOOK LEAVES
If the leaves of a book get torn, mend by pasting a piece of tracing paper over the tear.

A Granny saying: 'Good Health keeps you young.'

BRAN — For cleaning purposes

To make bran water: fill a small bag, such as an ordinary salt bag, with bran, place it in a pail, cover it with boiling water, and it is ready to use.

For painted and varnished woodwork it is invaluable, removing the dirt without destroying the finish. Coloured goods, which usually fade when washed, should not lose colour if washed in bran-water. It is excellent as a scalp cleanser, and is good for hair; making it very glossy. Used instead of soap it whitens and softens the hands. Bran is very useful.

BRASSES — Cleaning

Before cleaning brasses with polish, rub with a sliced lemon, and afterwards polish in the ordinary way with a soft cloth.

Badly tarnished brass should respond to the following mixture: 2 ounces each of salt, flour and vinegar shaken well together. Rub on, leave a short while, wash with warm soapy water.

BREAD
When cutting new bread, heat the knife in hot water and the bread will cut as smoothly as stale.

BURNING OIL — To extinguish
Flour freely sprinkled on burning oil will at once extinguish the flames.

CAKE MAKING AND PUDDINGS
Dredging: When making a rich fruit cake, always dredge flour over the fruit before adding it to the rest of the ingredients. this will prevent the fruit from sinking to the bottom of the tin while cooking.
Prevention of burning: To prevent cakes from burning when baking line a tin with greased paper as usual, and put in the mixture; stand the tray on a tin covered with salt. The salt will prevent the cake from burning and it will be a nice brown all over. The same wrinkle applies to milk puddings but leave out the greased paper. The pudding should not burn if baked on a tray of salt.

If your oven is inclined to burn, stand the tin in which you bake your cake either on a tin of hot sand or in another slightly larger cake tin, laying two sticks across the bottom.

Pudding Test: It is sometimes rather a difficult matter to decide whether a boiled pudding is completely done or not. Watch the pudding cloth and as soon as it begins to look wrinkled you may be quite sure that your pudding is ready to be removed from the pot.

CANDLES
A candle can be made to fit into any candlestick by dipping it into very hot water.

CARPETS
Laying: Before laying a carpet, rub the boards over with turpentine to safeguard it against moths.
Stair Carpet: Stair carpets should be swept with a wet broom. This will prevent the dust rising and causing the carpets to look brighter and cleaner than if done with tea leaves.

CHIMNEYS
If a chimney be on fire throw common kitchen salt on the fire and close the windows and doors in the room.

CHINA
Care of: Do not pour boiling or very hot water directly on to china as it can cause cracks..

Discoloured: The discoloration of teacups and other china can be easily removed if rubbed with kitchen salt, and after the stains are gone wash in the ordinary way.

To mend: To mend broken china beat lime into the very finest powder, and then sift through fine muslin. Then tie some into another thin muslin. Put on the edges of the china where broken some white of egg. Then dust some lime quickly on the edges, and unite them exactly.

CLOTHES LINES
Clothes lines(rope) are rendered much stronger and more weatherproof by boiling them for a quarter of an hour before using them at all.

COPPER KETTLE
Before cleaning a copper kettle fill it with boiling water and then the kettle will be found to clean much more quickly and easily than when cold.

CUT GLASS
To clean cut glass, wash articles, let them dry, and afterwards rub them with prepared chalk and a soft brush, carefully going into all the cavities.

CUTLERY

Fish Odour: A cut lemon rubbed over knives and forks will remove any odour of fish.

To clean rusty knives, stained handles: To clean rusty steel knives they should first be rubbed with a flannel dipped in paraffin, and then pushed up and down in garden mould and turf until all the rust is removed. Then wash and clean in the ordinary manner.

When polishing knives it is a good plan to hold the board to the fire a few minutes before beginning, as knives obtain a greater brilliancy on a warm board than on a cold one.

Stained knives may be cleaned by dipping a raw potato into brick dust and scouring them with it.

Stained knife handles: Discoloured knife handles may be cleaned by rubbing them with brick dust and vinegar.

To take the smell of onions from knives get a piece of carrot and draw a knife through it two or three times.

DINING TABLE

When white patches occur on tables through hot plates being placed on them, touch them up with a brush that has been dipped in spirits of nitre and directly afterwards rub them with a cloth moistened in sweet oil.

DISINFECTANT

Vinegar may be used as a disinfectant. If a little is burnt and sprinkled about a sickroom it will be both refreshing and agreeable.

EGGS

Eggs, when boiling, frequently burst. This is caused because they are too full of air and it may be prevented by pricking one end with a needle before putting them into the water, thus making an outlet for air.

A good egg will sink in water.

When frying eggs if you wish to prevent the spluttering and flying of the hot fat, sift a little flour in the pan before adding the eggs. If eggs crack in boiling, sprinkle a teaspoonful of salt into the water and then the whites will not come out.

ENAMEL BATH TUBS

Scrubbing enamel bath tubs with any soap containing sand will thin and eventually crack the enamel.

FINGER MARKS ON DOORS

Finger marks on doors may be removed by rubbing well with a piece of flannel dipped in paraffin.

FLOOR STAIN

A very good floor stain that will make your wooden floor quite beautiful and will last a lifetime can be made from a little glue and brown umber. Usually obtainable from an oil or paint shop (without any trouble in Gran's day). Boil the glue in a quarter of water, and when properly boiled, mix in the brown umber. When cool, paint evenly on the boards which have previously been scrubbed and are free of dust and dirt. When the stain is thoroughly dry finish with a coat of clear varnish and the floor should be as smooth as glass and have a beautiful polish.

FRUIT

Sour: Sour fruit will require less sugar for sweetening if, when it is stewed, a pinch of bicarbonate of soda is added to it to lessen the acidity of the juice.

Half rhubarb can be used with any kind of fruit without its being detected.

Raspberries —*To keep:* Spread raspberries out on a large platter and they will keep better than if put in a deep bowl.

FURNITURE DUST
To remove dust from around the buttons in furniture, take a pair of bellows and blow well around the buttons.

GLASS
Glass washed in cold water will have a bright and clearer appearance than when warm water is used.

Put a spoon in a glass when pouring hot or very hot liquid into it. Direct the liquid on to the spoon.

Wash each glass separately, otherwise water pressure can cause chips or cracks.

GLASSES (SPECTACLES)
Methylated spirits cleans spectacle glasses and makes them beautifully clear.
Rub with a clean cloth dipped in spirit; dry and polish with a bit of chamois leather.

HOT GREASE SPILLAGE
Should hot grease be spilled on the kitchen table or floor quickly pour cold water on it. This will cause it to harden quickly, and prevents it soaking into the wood.

JAM — To keep
A small pailful of lime should be kept in the cupboard with preserves to prevent them from moulding.

LAMP LIGHT — To improve
A small piece of camphor put in the reservoir of a lamp will improve the light.

LINOLEUM — To clean
Linoleum which is well polished once a week or once a fortnight and wiped with a rag slightly moistened with paraffin, and then rubbed well will last much longer then if it is frequently washed; and as an added bonus the polish will be preserved. If it gets very dirty, do wash it in clean water, but not with soap, and as soon as it is dry polish it with linoleum cream, for which the following is an excellent recipe.

LINOLEUM CREAM
A quarter of a pound of pure beeswax, a piece of yellow soap (about two inches square), half a pint of turpentine and half a pint of water. Shred the wax into a good sized jar, then pour the turpentine over it and let it stand for a day. Cut up the soap and boil it with the water, then mix all the ingredients together and leave the result until it is nearly cold. If this cream gets too stiff by being kept, add a little turpentine to it and remelt it by standing it in a pan of warm water.

MACHINE GREASE
Cool rainwater and soda will remove machine grease from most washable fabrics.

MATTING
To clean matting first sweep thoroughly with a stiff broom, following the grain of the straw. Then sweep across the grain with a soft broom that has been dipped in warm water. Then wash thoroughly in warm water in which a handful of salt has been dissolved. Nothing brightens coloured matting so much as the salt. And it also helps to prevent it from from fading. Light coloured matting should be washed in water in which borax has been dissolved. If any grease spots are noticed *before the matting is cleaned* cover them with a mixture of prepared chalk wet with turpentine, which, after being allowed to remain for two days,

should be removed with a stiff brush. Should the grease have been allowed to sink in, add about one eighth of washing soda to the mixture and this should despatch it. It is said that sweet milk will keep the matting in a good state of preservation and it is only required to use the application about once a year.

MEAT — Tough

To make tough steak tender hang it as long as it can be left in safety, washing it with vinegar every day. Take it down then, wipe with a clean dry cloth, put it upon a dish, and pour over it four or five spoonsful of salad oil and the juice of a large lemon. Put in a cool place for several hours, turn it over and over, that it may soak up every drop of oil and lemon and leave it for some hours longer.

If it is to be eaten at breakfast do it overnight. If for supper or late dinner, begin the preparation in the early morning.

When you are ready to cook the steak hold it up for a minute to let the surplus oil drop from it, but do not wipe it. It will be more juicy for the oil bath. Broil quickly over a clear fire, turning several times.

QUICK METHOD: When meat appears tough, add a tablespoonful of vinegar to the water or gravy it is cooked in, and simmer it very slowly.

MENUS
A menu for each meal made out weekly will save much anxiety and valuable time as to each day's catering.

MICE
Mice have a great dislike to the smell of peppermint, and a little oil of peppermint place around their haunts and holes will successfully keep the pests away. Fresh raw meat is the best bait for mouse traps.

MILK
To prevent boiling over: place in ordinary pie chimney in the centre of the pan of milk. When it comes to boil it boils up through the small chimney and there is not the slightest danger of it boiling over.

To prevent burning: Before putting the milk on to boil, rinse out the saucepan with water.

Burnt and scorched milk: Burnt or scorched milk may have its unpleasant taste entirely removed by the following process. The saucepan should be taken very carefully from the fire, so that the burnt part may not mix with the milk at the top, and placed in a pan of cold water until the bottom of the saucepan is quite cool then pour the milk carefully away leaving the burnt part at the bottom. But remember if a drain (small amount) of water be put in the bottom of the saucepan in which the milk is boiled the necessary stirring and watching to prevent burning will be done away with and the milk will boil without any trouble.

To preserve: Pour the milk into a bottle and place the bottle up to its neck in a saucepan full of water, which is then to be put on the fire and allowed to boil for a quarter of an hour. The bottle is now to be removed from the water and carefully closed with a good and tight fitting cork so as to render it as tight as possible.

Milk which has been preserved by this process has been kept for a year without turning sour.

To Prevent Going Sour: A tiny pinch of carbonate of soda put into the milk as soon as it arrives will prevent it going sour and is quite tasteless.

MIRRORS
Never hang a mirror where the sun's rays fall on it. The sun acts upon the mercury and clouds the mirror.

A good-sized mirror in a gilt frame will lighten a dark hall or room.

MOTHS
Whole cloves scattered plentifully among clothing in drawers and boxes will keep away moths as effectively as camphor.

To exterminate moths wring out a cloth in strong turpentine, and put among woollen goods. This will kill the pests.

Articles infested with moth should be saturated with benzine. This kills the insect and injures nothing.

MUD STAINS
Potato water is excellent for cleaning mud stains from nearly any kind of cloth or garment.

MUSTARD
Wet mustard first with a little vinegar before adding water (warm) to make it the right consistency.

ONIONS

To make onions digestible rinse several times in fresh additions of boiling water before they are cooked. They will be found to be more digestible when they are then cooked in the ordinary way.

PAPERED WALLS — Marks and stains

If marks and stains are on papered walls try French chalk on a piece of dry bread. Rub in gently.

Grease spots can be removed if French chalk wet with cold water is applied less than 12 hours after the mark is made.

PEARS — Preservation of

Rub pears over with a little grease or lard and store them away for winter use, piled together. They will not decay or rot.

A Granny saying:
'Content the corpse on whom the rain falls.'

PICKLES

When bottling pickles, boil the corks; while hot you can press them in the bottles and when cold they should be sealed tightly.

PIPE LEAKING — To stop a gas or water leak

Soap mixed with whiting will stop a gas or water leak in a pipe until a plumber can be sent for. Both types of leaks should be viewed seriously.

PLANTS

Plants whould be watered at least once daily. Do this after sundown for if the water is applied in the morning of a sunny day, half of it will be absorbed by the heated atmosphere.

A few drops of ammonia to a pint of water sprinkled on the roots of house plants will produce an abundant growth.

To water when absent: fill a large bucket with water and stand it on a low stool. Place plant pots around the base of the stool. Put one end of a bootlace firmly in the pot and tying a small stone to the other end of the bootlace put the weighted end in the bucket. The water will be slowly diverted into the pots.

POLISH

Boot: An excellent boot polish can be made by mixing ordinary cake boot blacking with milk. This renders leather soft and pliable and gives an excellent polish.

Shoe Polish: A little orange or lemon juice put on the blacking brush after it has been dipped in the blacking or polishing cream should give a brilliant shine to boots and shoes.

Piano: Equal parts of vinegar and paraffin oil make a better polish for a piano than any furniture cream may do.

POTATOES — Frosted

Potatoes that have been affected by the frost should be kept in a dark place for some days after the thaw has commenced. If thawed in daylight they rot.

PRESERVES

To prevent your preserves and jams from mildew, dip rounds of white paper in the white of an egg and put on the top of jars; cover closely and they will keep for a long time.

RUSTY KEYS AND LOCKS
Lay rusty keys and locks in paraffin oil and allow them to remain covered for some time. The oil will loosen the rust and enable it to be rubbed off easily.

SALT
When salt becomes caked in its receptacles put into them a pinch of ground arrowroot and the salt will remain perfectly dry and fine.

SARDINES
To skin: dip quickly in and out of boiling water; then the skin can be removed quite easily with a knife.

SCREW — to remove rusty screw
Hold a red hot iron to the head of a screw for a short time, and use the screwdriver while the screw is still hot.

SOAP SCRAPS
When a cake of soap has been used until it becomes so thin that it is liable to break, put it and a new cake of soap in hot water for two or three minutes and press firmly with the fingers. It should stick together and become part of the new cake.

Shred up half a breakfastcupful of soap ends (never mind about them being hard and dry), pour over two tablespoonsful of strained lemon juice, and set in a cool oven or on the stove, stirring now and then, till it melts to a kind of jelly. Then beat it up with one tablespoonful of fine oatmeal, and mould into a cake or ball.

This soap is too strong to use on the face but it is fine for the hands and arms.

STAINS
Fruit: Fruit stains may be removed from linen as follows; tie up some cream of tartar in the stained part and let it boil in soap suds for a few minutes. Then wash and rinse in clear water and the stain will be gone.

Paint on glass: Hot vinegar is commended as an effective agent in removing paint stains from glass.

Green on brick tiles or steps: To remove green stains caused by damp on brick tiles or steps scrub well with water in which a small quantity of chloride of lime has beeen dissolved.

STOVE BLACKING

Turpentine and vinegar mixed with black lead, and applied in the usual manner to stoves will produce a brilliant polish.

To prevent stove blacking turning brown: Mix ammonia with the stove blacking.

A stove which has been blackened can be kept in excellent condition by rubbing it every morning with a newspaper.

TENNIS BALLS

Rub them hard on a rough door mat and they will look like new.

TILED FLOOR

Wipe tiled floors over twice a week with skimmed milk, and once in two months polish with linseed oil and a soft cloth.

VEGETABLES

Rapid boiling dissipates the flavour and spoils the colour of vegetables.

General rule: Cook vegetables that grow below the ground with the lid on and those that grow above the ground without the lid.

WAX POLISH

One part yellow wax and two and a half parts of turpentine make a simple floor wax.

Apply with a brush and polish with a woollen cloth.

WINDOWS — Cleaning panes

Wash your windows with ammonia, hot water and a sponge. And then be sure to dry them with an old newspaper.

Fly marks on window panes can easily be removed if the glass is smeared with turpentine.

WOODEN TABLE TOPS

When white patches occur on tables, through hot plates being placed on them, touch them up with a brush that has been dipped in spirits of nitre; and directly afterwards rub with a cloth moistened with sweet oil.

A Granfy saying:
'If a job is worth doing, it is worth doing well.'

WRINKLES FOR CLOTHES AND TOILET CARE

ARTIFICIAL FLOWERS
If crushed or faded-looking, they can be made to look good again by holding them over the steam of a boiling kettle.

ASPARAGUS WATER
The water in which asparagus, white onions or lettuce has been boiled is said to cleanse the pores, stimulate the glands, and whiten the skin.

BLACK CASHMERE — To clean
Black cashmere may be cleaned by washing in hot suds containing a little borax. Rinse in very blue blueing water and iron while damp.

BLACK LACE — To renovate
Black lace unless very dirty and soiled should not be washed, but simply well shaken to remove the loose dirt and then dipped in a solution of deep blue gum water.

When black lace becomes very dusty and brownish in colour it is best to wash it in soap lather, then rinse and stiffen it in deep blue-water too which gum water has been added. The deep blue-water helps restore the black to its original appearance. The lace should be rolled in an old clean cloth for a short time, then pinned out with the same cloth between it and the sheet, as it imparts a blue stain which would necessitate the sheet being washed.

When the lace is quite dry the pins should be removed, and a piece of tissue placed over it. Iron with the paper between the lace and the iron thus avoiding making a gloss on the surface of the lace. A good method and also a very simple one is to dip the lace in a solution of equal proportions of milk and water. After squeezing out, the lace should be rolled in a cloth for a few minutes, then straightened and placed between folds of tissue-paper and ironed until dry.

The above proportions of milk and water make the lace very stiff, but if only a slight stiffness is required the proportion of milk should be reduced.

BLOUSE — To secure inside skirt
Obtain a piece of broad elastic, black or white and sew a hook and eye on it. Put it over the blouse into position. You will find it keeps the blouse better in place.

BLOUSES — Net
How to wash: Put a small amount of bran in a bag and tie it securely. Pour over three or four pints of boiling water; let it stand until cool. Put half of if it in a basin with sufficient soap jelly to make a lather. Dip the blouse in it and squeeze, but do not rub or it will tear. Add some cold water to the remaining bran-water, and rinse the blouse. Roll up in a cloth and iron while fairly damp with

a rather hot iron, press firmly on the wrong side,and place in front of fire to stiffen. This is a really good way to wash net blouses.

BOOTS — Tight

The solution to tight boots is far from difficult. Put the boot on and lace or button it up. Now stand the feet for a minute or two in a bath containing an inch or less of water. Then walk about until they are dry, and repeat if necessary. Naturally this should not be overdone and the feet allowed to get wet. This plan also cures 'squeaky' boots. The appearance of the boots should in no way be spoiled.

BOOT AND SHOE LEATHER — Care of

Never, never put boots away when they are wet. And do not ever dry them by or near a fire. Turn them on their sides in a cool, dry room; and if you do not have any shoe trees, stuff them with paper after taking them off.

Like people, leather needs a little nourishment occasionally. Neatsfoot oil is the best oil to use, and should be well rubbed in about once a month. A very little of the oil being necessary, and this most energetically applied until the leather has absorbed it. This is excellent for patent leather as well as for other kinds.

Do not shut boots and shoes up in a cupboard for they need air (just like people) if they are to wear well. Clean them at least once a fortnight even if they are not being used otherwise they are apt to get stiff and cracked. Two pairs of boots or shoes if worn alternately will last far longer than if worn day after day.

It is quite good and sensible plan to buy shoes six months before they are required, for leather toughens by being kept. Good furniture polish - provided you stick to the same one (it is not a good idea to keep chopping and changing about) — will be good for leather shoes.

Mudstains clean off best with a woollen cloth and vaseline. Do be generous with the vaseline, andd put the boots on trees or stuff out with paper ... crumpled newspaper is fine; then leave overnight. Next day black them over (if they are black), and they will look fine.

Shoe trees not only preserve the shape of the boot or shoe but they also preserve them.

BROWN NECK — To whiten

Take an ounce of glycerine and add the juice of a fresh lemon. Rub this into the neck for three nights with a piece of cotton wool. If the neck is very much discoloured try using an oatmeal poultice as follows:

Oatmeal Poultice: Put a breakfastcupful of oatmeal to soak in boiling water for two hours, then re-heat the oatmeal, pour off the water, add a teaspoonful of borax and a dessertspoonful of almond oil. Put the poultice in a piece of soft muslin, bind it around the neck. Later bathe with equal parts of water and eau-de-Cologne.

BUTTONHOLES

All buttonholes intended to bear great strain must be cut in the direction of the pull.

> *A Granny saying:*
> *'Do your washing on New Year's Day*
> *And you'll wash a relative away.'*

COMPLEXION

Lotion: A lotion for the complexion can be made by mixing four drachms of zinc oxide, two drachms of sulphur praecip., four drachms of glycerine, bringing it with rose water, up to four ounces.

Apply night and morning after washing the face with tepid water and oatmeal. Dry the face with a soft towel, and use clean cotton wool for gently dabbing the lotion on.

Care of: To make the skin beautifully fine and clear, wash your face in warm buttermilk instead of water and do not use any soap at all. Scalded buttermilk will keep sweet for several days.

To whiten the skin: To try to cure redness, roughness and blotchiness of the face make a paste of fresh fuller's earth and new cream. Make the paste just thin enough to spread. Apply it at night, and in the morning bathe the face with hot, soft water; or warm milk is better still.

Or: Rub cold porridge on your hands and face and see how it improves your complexion. Snow also is beneficial.

CLOTHES — To prevent blue streaking
Mix one dessertspoonful of soda with blueing water.

CORSET STEELS
Very few women seem to realise that the cause of broken corset steels is, in many cases, rust! The rust is, of course, the result of perspiration. To women who are troubled in this way this wrinkle may be of interest and help. Put a strip of chamois leather the width of the broader shields, and sew down securely on both sides the whole length of the steels. If this plan is stuck to, the number of broken steels will be reduced to a minimum and the saving of the underclothing from rust and stain will accordingly be very joyful.

ELDERFLOWER WATER
When elderflowers are in blossom a good supply of elderflower water should be made and bottled for use during the summer months. For it is so absolutely splendid for the hair and the complexion. Put about half a pound of freshly picked elderflowers into a jug or jar with one pint of boiling water, cover closely, set in saucepan of boiling water and simmer gently for several hours. Strain through muslin and, when cool, put into a perfectly clean bottle that has been rinsed out with eau-de-cologne, cork it closely. It will keep sweet and good for a week or two in this way, or for several weeks, if a wineglassful of eau-de-Cologne is added to every pint of elderflower water.

If distilled water is used the elderflower water should keep well for years if corked.

FURS

Written here are a few hints which will be useful during the cold weather. To clean furs heat one pound of oatmeal in the oven, then rub this well into the fur with a piece of clean flannel. If furs or other types of clothing are enclosed in a box with a little oil of turpentine, they will remain free from tiresome, destructive moths. *To clean swansdown:* first squeeze the down in a warm soapy lather, rinse in fresh cold water, and, after, shake the water out, hang in the air to dry.

GREASE SPOTS

Petrol is a splendid thing for removing grease or any other stains from dress material. If you dip a piece of flannel in petrol, and rub the least little bit, the mark will disappear. It will neither affect the dye nor leave any marks whatever, as soap and water does. You can purchase petrol at almost any cycle shop in small quantities. As this is highly inflammable it must not be used anywhere near gas or fire. Another good thing for cleaning a skirt is ammonia. Dip a little piece of flannel in ammonia and water and rub the soiled skirt down. It will take all the dust and dirt from it, leaving it quite fresh again. The following is excellent for removing grease marks from a coloured cloth. Apply a good layer of fuller's earth on the mark, allowing it to remain on for three or four hours, longer if necessary. When a good result has been obtained, brush the powder out of the skirt which will be found to be free of any objectionable stain.

GREASY SKIN

To cure and prevent this wash your face with very hot water and sluice with cold.

Then after drying, sponge it with this lotion: four tablespoonsful of elderflower water, half a teaspoonful of simple tincture of benzoin, added drop by drop, stirring all the time, five drops of pure glycerine and five drops of tincture of myrrh. ·

This is very soothing and refreshing, especially in hot weather.

A Granny saying:
'The Lord don't pay his debts in money.'

HAIR — Fair

A shampoo that helps to enhance fair hair, cleaning it very well besides making it soft and fluffy is as follows:

> *1 ounce of salts of tartar*
> *2 tablespoonsful of lemon-juice*
> *1 quart of hot rain water*

Put the salts of tartar into a bowl, pour over the lemon juice, then add the heated rainwater stirring it well. Wash the scalp and hair, and then rinse in plenty of lukewarm water.

If possible wash your hair outside on a warm sunny day and dry it with hot towels.

HAIR — Wavy

A reasonably priced and good mixture for keeping the hair wavy, even in wet weather, is one tablespoonful of glycerine mixed very gradually with six teaspoonsful of fluid ammonia.

Just dampen the hair before putting it into waving pins.

A solution of sugar and water will induce waves and curls.

A Granny saying:
'Colour of skin don't matter, colour of heart do.'

HANDS — To whiten

> *Strained juice of a lemon*
> *1 tablespoon of glycerine*
> *2 tablespoonsful of eau-de-Cologne or rosewater*

Mix it all together, rub over your hands — wet hands — then rub them together briskly until they are nearly dry. Wipe them on a soft towel, then dust on a little powdered starch or fuller's earth.

At night, the lemon mixture can be used again on dry hands. Just rub well in. This will whiten the hands and keep them smooth and nice.

CROWN OF A HAT

The crowns of hats or a hat can be restored to its original shape by dampening with cold water, stuffing with paper, and putting to dry in a hot place.

LACE — To starch old lace

Water in which rice has been boiled makes one of the best starches for old lace.

MOTHS — *see* page 38

NAILS — to prevent split

It is unfortunate but some nails are so brittle that they are always splitting or forming inflamed hang nails. To prevent and cure this, make a cream by melting one ounce of vaseline (white vaseline), half an ounce of pure lanoline and one drachm of powdered gum tragacanth in a jar. Stand this in a vessel of hot water.

Stir until thoroughly mixed, then add one tablespoon of rose water, remove from the heat and stir until nearly cold.

Steep the nails every night in warm alum water (one ounce of powdered alum to a pint of water). Dry and then apply the cream freely.

PAPER PATTERNS — Care of

Paper patterns can easily become mixed up unless they are marked in some way so that all the different pieces of one pattern can be clearly distinguished from those of another. One of the most successful ways is to mark each piece when the pattern is first unfolded so that it is immediately marked with the name or initial of the article for which it is a guide.

RELINING A COAT

First remove half the old lining to use as a pattern by which to cut out the new one, leaving the other half stitched to the coat to use as a guide. Unpick the pieces of lining which have been detached, lay them flat on the new material and cut around the pattern leaving enough for turnings. Sew up the seams leaving the arm seam free and open. Lay the new lining over the side of the coat and baste it into position, unpicking the remaining half by degrees, and basting the new in its place.

The bottom, front and neck must now be neatly hemmed and the armholes sewn up. Finally the linings of the sleeves must be sewn up and stitched in.

RIBBONS (HAIR RIBBONS)

To keep them fresh, wind them, when not in use, around a smooth glass bottle, fastening the ends with pins to keep them in place until required.

RIBBONS —To stiffen

Starch spoils ribbons, as it so soon makes them look old and worn. The best thing to use for stiffening ribbons or lace is to put several lumps of sugar in hot water and let them dissolve, then put the ribbons or lace in the water. This should provide them with just the right amount of stiffness.

SACHETS — Perfumed

Rose leaves dried thoroughly in the shade and then mixed with pounded cloves and mace and put into bags make a delicious perfume for the linen cupboard.

Orris root, ground or pounded, makes a nice perfume for sachets. Florentine orris root is the best.

SATIN SHOES — To clean

They may be cleaned very satisfactorily. Take a piece of flannel and dip it into spirits of wine, then rub the shoe with the grain of the satin, changing the flannel every time it becomes dirty. This process will not only clean white shoes but any light-coloured ones. It should be noted that white satin should always be kept in blue paper to prevent discoloration.

A Granny Saying: 'One thing's certain; you'll never get out of this life alive.'

SERGE SKIRT — Navy blue or black

To wash choose a really fine day, then place the skirt in sufficient cold water to cover it well, peel and slice four large potatoes and put in with the skirt. Let the skirt and potatoes stand for a couple of hours, then place the skirt on a table or washboard, and rub any marks with a piece of raw potato, rinse well through two lots of cold water, then place skirt while wringing wet on a coat hanger or failing this peg it on the line and place a short piece of stick across to hang it in a proper position, and let it drain until dry. The skirt should be hanging as though on the body and so should dry in its proper shape. Press all seams and press on wrong side with a warm iron. This will even improve a very shabby skirt.

SILK (TUSSORE) RENOVATION

To wash tussore silk, use bran water and no soap. Boil a pound of bran in two quarts of water, strain and add to the washing and rinsing water. Three parts of liquid to one of water are the right proportions for the mixture. Slippers, bags and belts will be cleaned by using French chalk. Potato water should be used for renovating ribbons for hair and hats, and the water should be tepid and very little soap employed.

Potato Water: Put scraped potato in hot water, and then strain it. In the case of a ribbon in the potato water, wash it gently with the fingers, wring it dry with a towel, and then iron it between cloths.

TO RENOVATE SHABBY SILK UMBRELLA

A silk umbrella when shabby can be renovated by sponging it with stale beer or porter.

If a piece of black sticking plaster is stuck over a hole in an umbrella on the inside it will look far neater than a darn.

SILK

To brush: A pad covered with velvet is far better for cleaning the dust from silk than a clothes brush.

Washing white or cream silk: When washing white or cream silk never use soap or soda for it turns it yellow.

WHITE SILK

To wash white silk needs much care. If very dirty it should be steeped in warm water in which a little borax has been dissolved. Then wash in warm water and soap jelly. Never boil silk or use very hot water.

SPONGE

Slimy: To clean a slimy sponge place the sponge in sufficient lukewarm water to cover and rub into the sponge one or two handfuls of common salt. Leave for a few minutes, then rinse well. The sponge will then be quite free from slime, and as good as new. This is a very useful method.

Hard sponge — to soften: Put enough cold water to cover the sponge in a saucepan quite free from grease. Add a large spoonful of borax. Drop in the sponge and bring the water to the boil. Then take out the sponge, rub some borax well into it and rinse in cold water.

A Granny saying: 'Be careful. Bare arms be bad for 'ee. They do attract colds and the men.'

STOCKINGS
Iron silk stockings embroidered fronts with a warm iron to make them bright and shiny.

SUNSHADE, LINEN — To clean
Open it wide and scrub it with a little scrubbing brush and good soap suds made of white soap and luke warm water. After it is well cleaned, pour several buckets of clean water over it,and, last of all, add a little blueing water poured from a watering pot; then leave it to bleach and dry it in the sunshine. All the work should be done outdoors preferably in sunshine because this would make the parasol clean and white in the end.

SUNSHADE — To wash
Open the sunshade and have ready a basin of warm water, a piece of hard soap and a nailbrush. Rub the soap thickly on the brush, moisten it with water and carefully brush the sunshade on the outside, paying special attention to the dirty crease that almost certainly runs up the middle of each division. Also brush it carefully round the top with as little pressure as possible. When the outside has been cleaned the sunshade should be reversed and placed on the table and each division brushed on the inside. The soap must be removed by pouring clean water over it. Leave the shade open until it is quite dry.

TOOTH POWDER
A good and safe tooth powder which makes the teeth beautifully white and keeps the gums in good order is made thus: Put one ounce of powdered chalk, powdered orris root, camphorated chalk and one drachm of powdered quinine together. Mix really well. Tepid water is best for cleaning and rinsing the teeth, as hot water is apt to make the gums tender, and cold may cause toothache. Soot can also be used to clean one's teeth; or kitchen salt.

TORTOISE-SHELL ORNAMENTS, COMBS, ETC.
Tortoise-shell ornaments etc. may be polished by rubbing them with pulverised charcoal and water, using a clean flannel cloth. Next moisten the article with vinegar, and rub with whiting and water. Afterwards polish with a soft cloth.

VEILS

Care of: A veil when it is taken off should be carefully rolled, not folded. Rolling is the way to keep it in good shape and let it come out fresh when it is next worn. It should be kept in mind that black veils, if they are worn for a long time, can become very dirty and are bad for the complexion.

Sight impaired by: It is likely that veils can produce short sight and even worse. Every description of veil afffects more or less the ability to see distinctly both in the distance and near at hand. Dotted veils are likely to be the most injurious. Continual looking through veils require that the eyes have to be focussed abnormally and could eventually, as a result, produce defective sight.

A Granny saying: 'Misery is infectious; so is happiness. Which are you going to spread?'

VELVET

Velvet so easily creases that it is an extravagant article to use. A grease spot or a stain caused by wear may be removed by turpentine rubbed on briskly with a piece of flannel.

Two or three applications may be necessary. The pile of velvet and velveteen may be raised by stretching it tightly over the top of a basin holding boiling water, and stroking it gently in the opposite direction with a soft brush.

Most velveteens will wash not once, but many times, if they are handled properly.

Put them through two lathers of warm soapy water, using a moderately stiff brush along the pile as the material lies stretched on the washing board. Rinse in cold clear water, to which has been added salt, and hang dripping wet in a shady place to dry. Do not squeeze or rub, but, if dirty, use the brush liberally.

VELVETEEN

Velveteen should be washed in lukewarm water with a lather of soap and really treated in the same way as flannels; but it is very important to remember it should not be rung by twisting. The water should be removed, preferably by pressure, as twisting is more than likely to induce a shaded appearance in the fabric. After the water is removed, the velveteen should be well shaken, and hung in front of a fire with the right side towards the heat, which will raise the pile as the water passes away. When it is quite dry, it must be placed on a thick blanket and ironed carefully on the wrong side. As a rule, this treatment makes velveteen look very good.

WATER — To soften
If you cannot get rain-water for toilet purposes, use oatmeal to soften the water. Do not throw it in loosely but tie up a bit in muslin allowing half a teacupful to a gallon and let it soak in the water some hours before using.

WATER SOFTENER for my lady's toilet
Fill a bottle such as you require two thirds full of distilled water, add borax a little at a time until you have used the water amd all the borax has dissolved. Keep this handy on the washstand whenever the face or hands are to be washed pour a tablespoonful into the water. This will soften the water and help to keep the skin smooth, soft and white. It also has healing properties. Add four tablespoonsful to a bath which is two thirds full of water and it will be found to be most soothing and beneficial.

WHITE WOOLLEN SHAWLS — To clean
Put the shawl into an earthenware pan and sprinkle it well with dry flour. Then take the shawl in both hands and rub it lightly all over. After rubbing well shake it thoroughly until all the flour is out. Repeat this process twice, when the shawl will look equal to new.

A Granny saying:
'If it wasn't for God I'd be an atheist.'

WRINKLED HANDS
Try rubbing them with fat from an uncooked chicken - or better still draw (disembowel) a few chicken.

At Christmas time hands were like softest silk after drawing chicken.

A Granny saying:
'Good manners are putting other people's feelings before your own.'

RECITES

SAVOURY

BEAN FEAST

One quart of beans
Two quarts of water
Two onions
Some good dripping
Pepper and salt

Soak the beans for 24 hours. Drain, simmer until tender in the water. Put the dripping in a frying pan, slice and fry the onions in it. Put in the beans, season, and fry until crisp. This is very filling.

BOILED LEG OF LAMB (good ole leg o' lamb)

A small leg of mutton or half a large one
A few slices of bacon
Four small carrots
Two blades of mace
Two turnips
Two medium sized onions (each stuck with four cloves)
Enough water to cover

Trim off the knuckle end and all unnecessary fat. Line the bottom of a saucepan with slices of bacon, lay the mutton upon them and cover with more slices on top. Put in the vegetables, cut up, cover with cold water and stew gently for three hours. Then take up the meat and put in front of a fire to brown, basting it with a little stock. Meanwhile reduce the stock by rapid boiling, `strain` out the vegetables, thicken the stock and colour with a little browning; place the meat on a dish and pour the stock over. If liked, vegetables may be served with gravy. The meat will be very tender.

BRUSSELS SPROUT PUREE

One pound of brussels sprouts
1 pint milk
Pinch of soda; salt and pepper

Wash and trim one pound of brussels sprouts. Put them into a saucepan with plenty of fast boiling water to which has been added a tiny bit of salt and a pinch of soda. When the sprouts are tender, drain off the water, and rub the sprouts through a fine sieve. Put the pulp back in the pan, and add to it one pint of boiling milk and half a pint of boiling water to make the appearance of the thickness of good cream. After bringing to the boil, season most carefully with salt and white pepper. Serve very hot.

CABBAGE BALLS

Mix together some minced meat, parsley, onion, rice, pepper and salt, and bind the mixture together with a beaten raw egg. Steam some cabbage leaves in very little water, roll a little of the mixture into each one in the form of a ball, then lay them very carefully in a very large pan with about a breakfastcupful of water and let them steam gently for an hour and a half.

CHEESE CUSTARD

3 ounces of grated cheese
One pint of milk
Half an ounce of butter
3 eggs
2 ounces of breadcrumbs
Salt and pepper to taste

Well butter a pie dish. Beat the eggs together in a basin until they are frothy, then add the milk. Stir the cheese and breadcrumbs into the mixture, add salt and pepper. Then pour the mixture into a pie dish or you could use small souffle dishes. Put little knobs of butter on the top and bake in a moderate oven. Pie dish should take approximately three quarters of an hour but souffle dishes should require only ten minutes, or till the mixture is set and a good brown colour.

COD CAPERS

Half a pound of fish, free from bones
Quarter of a pound of mashed potato
Sauce — anchovy, parsley or melted butter or cream
Whites and yolks of two eggs
Brown breadcrumbs

Mince the fish really finely and mix it with the mashed potatoes; add the sauce or cream (a good spoonful). Bind the mixture together with the egg yolks. Make into balls or cakes and dip into the whites of the eggs and brown breadcrumbs. Fry, and then serve on pieces of fried bread. Any cold meat or poultry can be used instead of fish.

A Granny saying: 'Happiness and serenity come from liking the people you do love.'

COLLARED HEAD

Half a pig's head
Two pig's feet
Two knuckles
Four pounds of shin of beef
Peppercorns
Whole allspice to taste
A little maize all tied in a little muslin bag
One onion stuck with cloves
A few cloves

Soak the cheek, feet and knuckles all night in cold water, scrape well and put together with all ingredients into a large saucepan and cover with cold water. Simmer slowly for five or six hours, till the meat comes clean off the bones, then cut the meat into small pieces, put into a large basin, strain the liquid onto the meat and return to the saucepan, stir well and boil up. Have ready some blancmange shapes and basins; fill with a soup ladle. Leave until cold when it will be a nice glossy shape.

CURRY BALLS

Quarter of a pound of any meat (cooked), minced very finely. Mix it with half a pound of boiled rice, a tablespoonful of curry powder, a little onion and apple minced, season with pepper and salt. Bind with a well beaten egg and form into balls. Dip each ball in breadcrumbs and fry in a nice brown boiling fat. Serve very hot.

FISH CREAM

> *Flaky white fish*
> *Buttered breadcrumbs*
> *Lemon juice, pepper and salt*
> *Four tablespoonsful of butter*
> *Two tablespoonsful of flour*
> *A pint of milk and a slice of onion to every pint of boned fish*

Boil the fish slowly for 20 minutes, take out the bones, separate the flakes, add pepper and salt and a few drops of lemon juice. *Butter sauce:* Melt butter in a saucepan, add the flour with a wooden spoon until perfectly blended. Allow the mixture to cook for a few minute and then add the milk and onion gradually, boil for three minutes stirring all the time. Pour the liquid over the flakes but gently, arrange in a pie dish, sprinkle with buttered crumbs, and bake in a hot oven for 20 to 30 minutes. Cod and hake are ideal for this very dainty supper dish.

FLEMISH CARROTS

Pare and slicce the carrots into strips, then cut them up exactly like kidney beans. Fill a stewpan with these, and put in a good piece of either butter or dripping. Cover closely and let them cook fast in their own steam for about half an hour, shaking them occasionally to prevent burning. When tender, put in a pinch of pepper and salt, a tablespoon of minced parsley and a tablespoonful of vinegar. Shake well and then let simmer for another five minutes. Serve very hot.

MOCK BOILED CHICKEN

A fresh hand of pork
Stuffing
Flour or cornflour

Use a fresh hand of pork, remove the bladebone and foot. Salt it for a day and a night. Before cooking wash off the salt, make some stuffing as for veal, and place it in the joint where the bone has been taken out. Roll up and tie with tape, making sure the ends are closed, otherwise the seasoning will boil out. Put in a saucepan with sufficient warm water to cover, simmer gently until tender.....this could be two hours or more according to weight. Make a thick sauce with cornflour or flour putting plenty of chopped parsley in it. Pour over the joint and serve.

This was a big favourite with the great aunts.

MOCK DUCK

This is an excellent cold dish for breakfast, and very appetising. Mince very finely and mix together two pounds of rump steak and two pounds of veal to which must be added half a pint of grated breadcrumbs and sufficient seasoning of chopped parsley and sage with pepper and salt. Mix the whites and yolks of three eggs with a suspicion of mustard, put them into the basin with the other ingredients and form the whole into a roll. Sprinkle this thickly with dried breadcrumbs, envelope it in buttered paper and bake for two hours.

MOCK JUGGED HARE

Lean steak
Butter for frying
Two cloves
One onion
Lemon rind, a bunch of sweet herbs, bay leaf

Cut the lean steak into small pieces and fry until brown in boiling butter. When brown place in a fireproof jar and pour over a little red wine, put on cover and leave for half an hour. Put two cloves into an onion and put in to jar with a strip of lemon rind, bunch of sweet herbs and a bay leaf. Cover with well-seasoned stock, put lid on jar and place in an oven to stew gently for two hours.

Fry golden brown some forcemeat balls for last quarter of an hour and put in a jar. Dish up steak on a very hot dish, garnish with the forcemeat balls and fingers of toast and redcurrant jelly.

OATMEAL BLANCMANGE

Oatmeal blancmange will make a breakfast in itself. Bring one pint of milk to the boil, add a teaspoonful of salt and stir in a cupful of oatmeal. Boil for 45 minutes; add a well beaten egg just before removing from the fire. Serve hot with cream and sugar, or cream alone. A bit of grated lemon or orange peel will improve the flavour.

PICKLED NASTURTIUMS

Gather the pods on a dry day, put them in a glass bottle and to each pint of vinegar add an ounce of salt and six peppercorns. The pods may be added from day to day. Bung up the bottles and seal the tops. The pickle should be made one season and used the next.

A Granny saying: 'Food should be eaten slowly, quietly and peacefully.'

RICE SAVOURY

Two tablespoonsful of rice
Lump of butter
Onion stuck with cloves
One egg
Grated cheese

Boil rice until tender with lump of butter the size of a walnut and the onion stuck with cloves. When cooked, take out the onion and add one egg well beaten and some grated cheese. Mix well and put in buttered dish. Dust a little more grated cheese on top and bake for 15 or 20 minutes.

ROAST PHEASANT

Always, but always tie a piece of fat bacon over the breast of the pheasant and wrap the bird in a piece of well buttered paper. Roast before a clear fire or in a quick oven, for about 40 or 50 minutes. The paper and bacon should be removed for the last 15 minutes so that the bird will brown. Toast a piece of bread over the fire rungs and then when the bird has been cooking for 30 to 40 minutes put the toast under the bird to catch all the gravy that drips from it. Stand the pheasant on a very hot dish on the toast

SHEEP'S HEART

1 sheep's heart
Half a teaspoonful of sage
1 onion
Half an ounce of breadcrumbs
Quarter of an ounce of flour
Salt, pepper, dripping and a quarter of a pint of stock or water

Peel and parboil the onions, chop finely; then mix together the onions, crumbs, sage(powdered), salt and pepper to taste. Wash the heart well in cold water and dry. Stuff with the mixture. Place in a meat tin, put some dripping over in small pieces and bake in a hot oven for one hour and a half. Baste frequently and when done put on to a hot dish. Mix the flour with the dripping, add quarter of a pint of water, stir until it boils, season, then strain around the heart.

SKATE AND CAPER SAUCE

Skate
Salt
Water
Vinegar
Liver
Half pint of melted butter
Two ounces of chopped capers

Roll up several pieces of skate and tie with white tape. Put in a pan where salt water is boiling, add a tablespoonful of vinegar. Boil gently until well cooked. A few minutes before the fish becomes well cooked put in the liver and boil for five minutes. Drain the fish and place on a hot dish.

Finely mince the liver. Stir the capers into the boiling melted butter. Pour the sauce over the fish and scatter the minced liver on the top.

SWEETBREADS

Calves' breads or lambs' breads for preference
Salt,onion, blade of mace, piece of lemon peel
A little milk, cornflour, nub of butter

Soak the sweetbreads in salt for two or three hours. Take them out, strain them and put them in a saucepan with the onion, one blade of mace, lemon peel and salt and pepper to suit. Let this neearly boil, skim thoroughly, then let it simmer most gently for three hours. Thicken the milk with a little cornflour, add the nub of butter. Cut the sweetbreads into tidy slices, and pour the hot sauce over.

VEGETARIAN CUTLETS

Take three carrots, three turnips and three onions that have all been cooked. Mash them together, then mix them with half a pint of cooked lentils which have been made as dry as possible. Flavour with curry powder and minced parsley. Bind the mixture with a beaten egg, mould into cutlets and brush over with egg and breadcrumbs. Fry until brown. This will be found to be a most enjoyable supper dish.

RECIPES

PUDDINGS AND SWEETS

APPLE CREAM

One and a half pounds of apples
Half a gill of hot water
One lemon
Two ounces of castor sugar
Half a pint of cream
Some redcurrant jelly
A little cochineal

Peel, core and slice the apples, then place them in a saucepan with the water, sugar and grated lemon rind. Let them stew gently till they are soft, then rub them through a wire sieve, after which beat them to a pulp with an egg whisk. Whip the cream stiffly and then stir the apples into it with a few drops of cochineal added to make it a pretty pink. The mixture should then be heaped up roughly in a glass dish and be decorated with a few heaps of redcurrant jelly.

BANANA CREAM

Two bananas
Two ounces of cornflour
Two yolks of eggs
One quart of milk
Two ounces of castor sugar
Half a teaspoonful of vanilla essence

Mix the cornflour with a little milk, put the rest of the milk into a stewpan with the sugar. When boiling add the blended cornflour and milk and boil for about ten minutes. Let the mixture cool for a little while, then add the vanilla essence and the bananas thinly sliced. when cool pour into a prepared mould. This dish takes about 20 minutes to prepare.

BANANA CROQUETTES

> *Bananas (ripe)*
> *Egg*
> *Breadcrumbs*
> *Fat*

Peel bananas, cut in two and cut off round ends. Egg and breadcrumb the bananas. Fry in deep fat and serve very hot.

BURNT CREAM

Boil a pint of cream with a stick of cinnamon and some lemon peel; take it off the fire and pour it very slowly into the yolks of three eggs, stirring till half cold; sweeten and remove the cinnamon; pour it into the dish. When cold, sprinkle castor sugar over and brown it with a salamander.

A Granny saying:
'Never cut the lawn on Good Friday.'

BUTTERCUP JELLY

Half an ounce of sheet gelatine
Cup of cold water
Cup of sugar
Cup of hot milk
Beaten yolks of two eggs
Vanilla
Egg whites

Soak the gelatine in a cup of cold water. Put it in a small basin and stand it over a saucepan of boiling water. Then add the sugar, hot milk and egg yolks. Flavour with vanilla to suit; set it on the stove and boil for one minute. Whip the whites of the eggs to a stiff froth, stir them into the jelly. When really thick pour into a mould. Turn out when cold.

CALVES' FOOT LEMON PUDDING

Boil four quarts of water with three calf's feet ot two cow heels that have only been scalded till the water is half evaporated; take the jelly from the fat and sediment, mix with it the juice of a Seville orange and twelve lemons, the peel of three lemons, the whites and shells of six eggs, brown sugar to taste, some sherry, one ounce of coriander seeds, a quarter of an ounce of allspice, a piece of cinnamon, all bruised. The jelly should boil 15 minutes without stirring,then clear it through a flannel bag. Take a little of the clear liquid and mix with a teacupful of water in which a portion of beetroot has been boiled; run it through the bag. This is to garnish the other jelly being cooled separately on a plate, but this is a matter of taste. This jelly has a fine colour and taste.

CANADIAN BLANCMANGE

Pound of red or blackcurrants, or similar fruit
Two ounces of cornflour
Sugar
Water

Stew the fruit with sugar and a little water. When the fruit is soft, strain the juice, measure it and add water to bring the liquid to three quarters of a pint only. Mix the cornflour with a quarter of a pint of cold water, add the fruit juice and boil gently for three minutes. Pour into a wet mould, when set turn it out and serve with fresh cream or boiled custard.

CANARY PUDDING

Two eggs and their weight in butter
Flour and castor sugar
One tablespoon of baking powdeer
One tablespoon of milk
Grated rind of one lemon

Grease a mould or basin thickly. Cream the butter and sugar together, then break and add the eggs to the mixture, beating well. Mix together flour and baking powder, then stir in lightly. Add the lemon rind,stirring all the while. Pour the mixture into the greased mould and steam for two hours. Turn out onto a pretty hot dish and serve with clotted cream.

CHESTNUT SURPRISE

Chestnuts
Half a pint milk
Vanilla
Sugar

Boil the chestnuts in water until soft enough to peel. Flavour the milk with vanilla and sugar, add the peeled chestnuts, then boil them until they are really soft. Sieve through a colander so that the mixture looks like vermicelli. Pile lightly on a glass dish, and serve with scalded cream.

A Granny saying:
'When my boot covers five daisies
I do know that Spring is come.'

CHOCOLATE CUSTARD

One pint of milk and a quarter of a pint of milk
Two teaspoonsful of cornflour
Two teaspoonsful of cocoa
One tablespoonful of sugar

Bring a pint of milk to the boil. Mix the cornflour with the quarter pint of millk. Pour this into the boiling milk and boil for five minutes. Mix the cocoa and sugar, then pour half a cup of boiling water on the cocoa mixture, stirring all the while. When completely dissolved pour onto the other mixture. Boil for two minutes, then pour into custard glasses and serve. Put a lump of clotted cream on each custard if you wish.

CRANBERRY JELLY

One quart of cranberries
Half a pint of water
One pint of granulated sugar

Cook the cranberries in the water for 20 minutes, then rub through a fine sieve and add the sugar. Cook ten, minutes longer. Do not add more or less of the liquid or sugar, or the jelly will not mould. It should boil all the time it is cooking. The moment it has cooked for ten minutes, turn it into a mould and put it in a cool place for 12 hours or more. Cranberries should always be cooked in porcelain.

DEANERY PUDDING (fit for a bishop)

A quarter of a pound of breadcrumbs
A quarter of a pound of flour
A quarter of a pound of suet
Two ounces of sultanas
Two ounces of sugar
One lemon rind and juice of lemon
One saltspoon of nutmeg
One tablespoonful of treacle
One teaspoonful of baking powder
A pinch of salt and a little milk

Chop suet, clean sultanas, make the breadcrumbs. Mix dry ingredients thoroughly, beat egg, add milk and mix together quickly.

Butter a mould, put in mixture, tie over with buttered paper and cloth and steam for two hours. Serve with custard.

DUCHESS PUDDING (fit for a queen)

Well grease a pudding bowl, and sprinkle thickly with currants. Cut some thin slices of bread and butter into neat shapes. Sprinkle currants between each slice. Do not quite fill the bowl with them. Then make a custard with two eggs and one pint of milk and two ounces of sugar, or half quantities if a smaller pudding is desired, and pour over the bread. Cover with butter paper and steam one and a half or two hours.

DUTCH PUDDING

Teacupful of carefully washed rice
One and a half pints of milk
Cupful of sugar
Half a pound of currants
Two ounces of butter
Grated rind of lemon (or candied peel if preferred)
Two eggs

Boil rice in the milk until thick, then add sugar, currants, butter, and lemon. Allow to grow cold, then add eggs (well beaten) and bake in a moderate oven for half an hour.

FLUMMERY

One pound of soft fruit
One and a half tablespoonsfuls oatmeal/cornflour
1 and a half cups of milk
Half a small cup of sugar
pinch of salt
1 beaten egg

Mix half the milk with the oatmeal, sugar and salt until smooth. Meanwhile bring the remainder of the milk to almost boiling point and add slowly to the mixture. Stir over medium heat until it thickens. Put beaten egg in large bowl and then slowly add mixture from the saucepan. Return mixture to the saucepan and cook for several more minutes, stirring constantly. Pour into a mould and when quite cold turn onto a dish and smother with the fruit.

FRUIT SALAD

Three bananas, two oranges, two peaches, some pineapple, a little of as many kinds of fruit as you can get, the more the better. Slice the bananas in circles, divide the oranges into sections, removing peel, pith and pips; skin the peaches and take out the stones from any fruit used. Large plums should be cut into slices. Add some of the pineapple syrup to the juice of the extra orange; sweeten with castor sugar and pour over the fruit. Cover with whipped cream and serve with imitation cream.

IMPERIAL PUDDING (fit for an Empress)

> *Six ounces breadcrumbs*
> *Six ounces cored and sliced apples*
> *Nutmeg*
> *Sugar to taste*
> *Egg*
> *Nub of butter*
> *Half a pint of milk*

Well grease a pie dish, throw breadcrumbs over the bottom and sides, put a layer of apples and grate some nutmeg, scatter a tablespoon of sugar (or more) over the apples, then a layer of crumbs, then apples, then crumbs, until you have exhausted your ingredients but ending with a layer of crumbs.

Mix the egg with the milk and pour over the pudding, put the nub of butter on the top and bake for three quarters of an hour. Turn out into a very hot dish.

MARBLE JELLY

One packet each of lemon jelly and raspberry jelly.
Some milk (two tablespoonfuls)

Dissolve the jellies in different basins. Pour half a pint of each into soup plates and set aside until firm. Mix the remainder of the jelly together and add the milk. This latter must be kept in liquid. When the jellies in the plates are set, cut into blocks, fill a wetted mould with them, and then pour on the liquid jelly. When the mould is set, turn out.

A very pretty sight will greet your eyes.

PEACH SPONGE

One ounce of gelatine
One tin of peaches
Whisked whites of three eggs
Juice of one lemon
Half a pound of lump sugar
Three gills of water

Soak the gelatine in hot water for ten minutes. Put into a stewpan the juice of the peaches, sugar, lemon juice and dissolved gelatine, making the liquid up to one pint. Stir over the fire until hot. Pour into a large basin; when beginning to set, add the whites of the eggs beaten to a stiff froth. Whisk until the preparation is light and spongy. Heap up lightly on a glass dish and serve with the peaches around the sponge. Fill the centre of the peaches with whipped cream, just slightly sweetened.

A Granny saying:
'A moment on your lips; a lifetime on your hips.'

QUINCE JELLY

The seed of the quince is very sticky. An ounce of bruised seed boiled with three pints of water will make three pints as thick as the white of an egg. Strain the liquid through a colander. To every pint put a pound of fine sugar; add grated orange or lemon peel then boil to a jelly. The pulp is not used.

RED APPLE JELLY

Pare and core some well-shaped apples; pippins or golden rennets if you have them but others will do. Throw them in a preserving pan, and with as little water as will cover them, let them simmer and when the lower side is done, turn them. Observe that they do not lie close when first put together. Mix some cochineal with the water and boil with the fruit. When sufficiently done, place them on the dish they are to be served in, stalk downwards. Take the water and make a rich jelly of it with loaf sugar, boiling the thin rind and juice of a lemon. When it has turned to a jelly, let it grow cold, and put it on and among the apples; cut the peel of the lemon in narrow strips and put it across the eye of the apple. Observe that the colour be fine from the first or the fruit will not afterwards gain it; and use as little of the cochineal as will serve, lest the syrup taste bitter.

ROWAN JELLY

The rowans should be quite ripe; pick them off the stalks, put them in the preserving pan and cover with water. Take them off the fire before they come to the boil; break with a woooden spoon and strain through a jelly bag. Add a pound of sugar for every pint of juice and boil until it jellies. Apples and rowans in equal quantities may be used if liked.

VANILLA SOUFFLE

Three yolks of eggs
One ounce of flour
One gill of milk
Half a teaspoonful of vanilla
Four whites of eggs
One ounce of butter
Two teaspoonsful of castor sugar

Thickly butter a souffle tin which hold one and a half pints. tie round outside the tin a band of buttered paper; this paper must stand up three inches above the tin and be of two layers so as to be strong. Melt the butter in a saucepan, add the flour and mix it smoothly.

Pour in the milk and stir till it boils, let it cook slowly for two or three minutes longer, stirring all the time. Take the pan off the fire and add the sugar. Let it cool a little, then beat in the yolks of eggs one by one. Beat the whites of eggs to a stiff froth and add them lightly to the yolks, flour, etc. Add the vanilla and pour the mixture into a tin. Put a piece of buttered paper over the top of the paper band and steam gently for about half an hour. Then turn out carefully on to a hot dish. Pour any good sweet sauce round, and serve at once or it sinks.

YORK CREAM (fit for a Princess)

Four large apples or more
Sugar to taste
A dollop of apricot jam
One ounce of arrowroot
One pint of cold milk
Half an ounce of butter
Small amount of breadcrumbs

Peel and core the apples, cut into slices and arrange in a pie dish; sprinkle with sugar, cover with a layer of apricot jam. Mix the arrowroot with the milk and butter and sweeten as suits. Stir this over the fire until it boils, then pour slowly over the mixture in the pie dish. Scatter the breadcrumbs over the top and bake until golden brown. This dish can be served hot or cold,for it is delicious either way.

YORK TARTLETS

Two ounces sugar
Two ounces butter
One tablespoonful of cornflour
Yolks of two eggs
Two ounces of ground almonds
White of egg
A little jam

Cream sugar, butter,cornflour, egg yolks and almonds together. Line some small tins with mixture. Put a little jam in bottom. Beat white of egg to a stiff froth then add to mixture. Put cross bar of pastry over each tart, brush with white of egg and dust with sugar. Cook in a moderate oven.

CAKES

BROWNEY BROWNEY CAKE

Half a pound of cornflower
Quarter pound of butter
One teaspoonful of baking powder
Half a pound of castor sugar
Three eggs

Mix cornflour, sugar and butter; slowly add the well beaten eggs, then add the baking powder and flavouring if liked. Put in small pans and bake until a light brown. If kept in a tin, these cakes will keep for a fortnight,and taste as nice as when new.

SEMOLINA CAKE

6 ounces of self-raising flour
3 ounces of semolina
A little milk
3 ounces of castor sugar
2 eggs
A quarter of a pound of lard or cooking butter

Mix the dry ingredients well together,then rub in the fat, add the eggs and milk well beaten. When thoroughly mixed, pour the mixture into a well greased cake tin and bake in a moderate oven for one hour.

SUGAR COOKIES

Cream half a cupful of butter, add a cupful of sugar and then gradually add the yolks of three eggs. Next add half a cupful of chopped almonds and, if liked, a pinch of aniseed. Mix to a dough just stiff enough to spread, with a cupful of and a third of flour sifted with a teaspoonful of baking powder. Spread in a buttered square pan, sprinkle with a mixture of sugar, cinnamon and chopped nuts and when baked cut into squares. These delicious little cakes will keep for quite some time.

SWEETS AND CANDIES

FUDGE

> *One dessertspoonful of chocolate powder*
> *Vanilla essence*
> *Two cupfuls of castor sugar*
> *Three quarters cupful of milk*
> *One ounce butter*

Boil all together till it will just set when dropped into cold water. Remove from the fire and beat with a wooden spoon till nearly cold; it should then be creamy. Pour on to a buttered plate or tin to set and make into fancy shapes when cold. It is important to beat it very thoroughly, as it candies if not continued long enough.

POPCPORN

Put some corn (Indian maize) in a wire basket over the fire, and shake about. As each corn bursts, remove it at once before it burns. Put three tablespoonsful of castor sugar, two tablespoonsful of water and one dessertspoonful of butter into a saucepan and boil for a few minutes, then put in the popcorn and stir till well mixed with the sugar. Remove from the fire and continue stirring till it cools, then remove the sugared popcorns and drain on a sieve.

FOR INVALIDS
AND CONVALESCENTS

ALBUMEN WATER
Take white of one egg, three tablespoons of water, salt or lemon juice to flavour. Whisk white to stiff froth, add water and leave until all dissolved. Add further flavouring if desired.

This is useful where milk cannot easily be digested.

ALMOND RESTORATIVE

6 bitter almonds
2 ounces sweet almonds
1 pint of milk
A little cream

Blanch and peel almonds. Pound to a paste with a little cream, then slowly mix in the milk. Strain and sweeten. This is a very nourishing drink.

ARROWROOT JELLY
Into a basin put a desserspoonful of arrowroot powder and mix as much cold water with it as will make it into a paste. Then pour on it half a pint of boiling water and stir briskly. It will become a clear, smooth jelly to which should be added two teaspoonsful of sugar.

A Granny saying:
'If you do want the soup to look good or as they posh ones do say, "You want to enhance its appearance", put a small lump of sugar into a clear soup when you are boiling it up and just before serving.'

CALF'S FOOT JELLY

> *2 calves' feet*
> *5 pints of water*
> *4 ounces of loaf sugar*
> *Half a gill of lemon juice*
> *1 gill of sherry*
> *The rind of 1 lemon*
> *White and shells of 2 eggs*
> *2 cloves*
> *1 inch of cinnamon stick.*

Cut the feet into four pieces, remove all marrow and fat, and blanch. Put them in a stew pan, add the water and simmer gently for six hours, skimming occasionally. Strain and measure the stock, if necessary boiling to reduce it to not more than a quart. Allow this to cool. Then remove all traces of fat. Replace jelllied stock in stewpan and add thinly peeled lemon rind, lemon juice, sherry, sugar, the crushed eggshells, stiffly whisked whites of eggs, the cinnamon and the cloves. Whisk while allowing to come to the boil, then simmer gently for ten minutes. Strain through a scalded jelly bag and turn into moulds which have been previously rinsed with cold water.

COW HEEL JELLY

1 Cow heel
3 Pints of water
2 Lemons
Whites and shells of 2 eggs
3 wine glasses of sherry
Sugar to taste

Put heel in a pan, add the water and simmer gently down to one pint. Strain and allow to cool. Remove all fat. Put the fluid back in the pan, add sugar, sliced lemons, the whites and shells of eggs, beat well; add wine; bring to the boil for one minute; remove from the fire and stand for a few minutes. Strain through a jelly bag or very fine muslin into a wetted mould.

CREAM JELLY

When an invalid is recommended to take cream and is quite unable to take it raw, a very good way of giving it is in the form of a jelly. Dissolve a half point jelly in less than half a pint of nearly boiling water, stir the jelly until quite dissolved and when it is nearly setting and becoming cool pour in the cream, as much as you wish. Stir until the cream is well mixed and put in a cold place to set. This is a most nourishing dish.

EGG JELLY

1 ounce of leaf gelatine
1 pint of water
1 lemon
Quarter of a pound of castor sugar
The yolks of 5 eggs

Dissolve the gelatine in the hot water, then add the lemon peel and sugar and let it come to simmering point. Be sure to have ready in a basin the yolks of five eggs, well beaten, and add to them the contents of the stew pan, adding also the juice of a lemon. Strain through muslin into a mould. A very nourishing jelly.

INVALID PUDDING

Half a pint of milk
A small piece of lemon peel
1 large teaspoonful of arrowroot
1 teaspoonful of sugar
1 egg

Put the milk and lemon rind in a pan, let it get quite hot, mix arrowroot to a paste with a little cold milk, remove the lemon rind and pour the remainder of the milk on to the arrowroot. Add the sugar. Let the pudding cool, then stir in the yolk of one egg, beat the white of the egg to a stiff froth and stir in lightly just before pouring it into a buttered pie dish and brown slightly in the oven. This pudding can be eaten hot or cold.and is very tasty.

MILK TEA

Milk tea is an excellent substitute for milk, when milk cannot be digested. Place the tea in an infuser or coffee strainer. Hold this over a cup and pour on boiling milk. The milk extracts the flavour from the tea, but not the tannin, so it is not injurious to the sick person but indeed is very nourishing.

RAW BEEF TEA

One pound of beefsteak cut thickly; place on a chopping board and holding it steady with a fork,scrape well with a large spoon. The particles of meat thus scraped should be placed in a basin, making sure no fat or skin slips in by mistake. Cover the meat with a pint of tepid water and allow it to stand for five hours on the hearth. At the end of that time strain through a muslin bag and give the liquid to the patient in doses of half a wineglassful.

A Granny saying:
'To defeat rheumatism carry a potato in your pocket'

BISCUITS

KRINGLES
Take the yolks of three eggs and whites of two eggs. Beat them well and mix with two ounces of butter just warmed. With this knead half a pound of flour and two ounces of sugar to a paste. Roll into thick biscuits; prick and bake them on tin plates.

JUMBLES
Mix six ounces of castor sugar with one pound of flour and one ounce of ground ginger. On these pour six ounces of butter and three quarters of a pound of treacle,which have been heated together to boiling point. When the paste is sufficiently cool, knead it very smoothly and roll it out thin on the tin upon which it is to be baked. Mark it with the back of a knife in squares, set it into a slow oven, and let it remain till it is quite crisp, without allowing it to take much colour. Divide while it is still warm, and as soon as it is cold put it into a dry canister.

SODA BISCUITS

3 pounds of flour
1 pound of butter or lard
1 pound of powdered sugar
1 and a half teaspoonsful of carbonate of soda
Half a pint of milk

Mix all the ingredients together, roll and cut very thin, bake in a quick oven. Sift sugar over top before baking. A very few drops of lemon or almond flavouring can be added.

BEVERAGES

CANADIAN OATMEAL WATER

Put four ounces of oatmeal into a basin with six ounces of white sugar and a large lemon cut into small pieces. (Peel the lemon first). Moisten with a small quantity of warm, not boiling, water. Stir for a few minutes then set aside to cool. When the oatmeal has quite settled, pour off the liquid into a pitcher ready for use. This is a most refreshing drink which is both thirst-quenching and strengthening.

ELDERFLOWER CHAMPAGNE

> *5 or 6 heads of elderflower*
> *1 and a half to 2 pounds of white sugar*
> *2 tablespoonsful of white wine vinegar*
> *1 gallon water*
> *1 lemon*

Pick the heads when in full bloom. Dissolve the sugar in about one quart of warm water. Pour into a large jug or container and make up the liquid to one gallon with cold water. Add the wine vinegar, and float the flower heads (stems upwards) and thinly sliced lemon on the top. Stand for about four or five days until mould begins to form, making sure the jug is covered to prevent fruit flies contaminating the wine. Strain through muslin and pour into clean bottles and cork. Delicious, and virtually non-alcoholic.
WARNING: Do not use screw tops. Corks will tend to fly off while maturing; replace and wine should be ready in a fortnight.

GINGER POP

Take four gallons of water, add two ounces of ginger. Boil for half an hour. Then add two and a half pints of clarified sugar. Let it boil for ten minutes longer. Take off the scum, put the liquor into a large bowl or cooler and let it stand until 'new milk' warm, then cask it, putting into the cask the rinds and juice of four lemons and a quarter of an ounce of isinglass previously dissolved in half a pint of warm water and a dessertspoonful of good yeast. Bung up the cask, set it in a cool cellar for ten days when the 'pop' will be ready to bottle. It should be strained carefully and must be bottled in stone bottles with wire tied over the corks.

HEALTH LEMONADE

> *4 lemons*
> *1 ounce of flour of sulphur*
> *4 quarts of boiling water*
> *Half an ounce of cream of tartar*
> *Half a pound of sugar*

Peel the lemons thinly, squeeze out all the juice. Put the sugar, juice, rind, sulphur and cream of tartar into a large jug. Pour over the boiling water, stir well,cover up. When wanted for use strain, for the sulphur floats on the top. This will keep two or three days if stored in a cool place.

LEMON BARLEY WATER

Peel three lemons very thinly and lay the peel in a large jug with two ounces of castor sugar and three ounces of pearl barley. Pour on to this three pints of boiling water and let it stand for 24 hours. Then add the strained juice of the lemons and stand on ice till wanted.

LEMON POWDER

> *Half an ounce of tartartic acid*
> *3 ounces of loaf sugar*
> *Half a drachm of essence of lemon*

Mix the acid and the sugar, pounding them very fine; pour on the essence of lemon, a few drops at a time. When all is mixed, divide into 12 equal parts and put them in white paper like powders. When required dissolve one in a tumbler of water and lemonade will be the result.

WINTER DRINK

1 pound of loaf sugar
1 quart of boiling water
Threepennywirth of peppermint essence (1900 price)

Put the sugar into a jug, add the essence of peppermint and cover with one quart of boiling water. Stir until thoroughly dissolved and then allow to cool. When cold, bottle and cork tightly. It will be ready for use in a few hours.

INCIDENTALS

BOTTLED LEMON JUICE

Buy lemons when they are cheap and keep them in a cool place for two or three days. Roll them so that they will squeeze easily. Squeeze the juice into a bowl, and strain it through muslin. Pour the juice into half ounce and quarter ounce bottles which are perfectly dry; fill them nearly to the top, then into each put half a spoonful of salad oil. Cork tightly and put in a cool, dark place. When you want to use the lemon juice, open a bottle containing as much as you need. Wind a little absorbent cotton on a skewer and dip it in to take up the oil. The juice will be just as fine as when first bottled.

FRUIT SALAD DRESSING

The juice of 3 lemons
2 oranges
Half a cupful of sugar
1 cupful of cream

Beat the juice of the oranges and lemons together, add sugar and boil until clear. Whip the cream and stir thoroughly into the mixture. Put on one side to cool. Pour over salad.

IMITATION CREAM

Mix a tablespoon of custard powder with a little cold milk, then add sufficient boiling milk to make it the same thickness as cream. Put it into a jar and place a pan of boiling water and stir for 15 minutes or more until cooked. Then sweeten to taste, and set aside to cool.

HEALTH FOR BABIES AND CHILDREN

WALKING

Walking is the healthiest exercise in the world. If the weather is wet. regular walking exercises round the nursery or up and down a corridor should be insisted on.

TABLE MANNERS

Children learn best from copying or teaching others. Imitate a dolls' manner class and let the little ones give a dolls' dinner party. Tell them that dolly is doing something naughty and encourage them to correct their dolls for the very habits they indulge in themselves.

EARLY TRAINING IN SLEEPING HABITS

Train little baby to go to sleep as soon as he is put into his crib. Once he has been made to understand that he will not be rocked and sung to, he will, as a rule, go to sleep the moment his head touches the pillow, or,if not quite at once, will lie still and amuse himself until he drops off.

A Granny saying:
'Babies and small children be arm aching. As they gets older they can be heartaching.'

Some titles from the **COUNTRY BOOKSHELF**:

GRAN'S OLD-FASHIONED GARDENING GEMS
Jean Penny
96 pages; Charmingly illustrated with period engravings;
Price £3.50

LETTERS FROM THE ENGLISH COUNTRYSIDE
Ralph Whitlock
160 pages; illustrated with pen & ink drawings; Price £4.95

O WHO WILL MARRY ME? *A Book of Country Love*
Ralph Whitlock;
80 pages; illustrated with Bewick engravings; Price £3.50

MAISIE AND ME: *A Country Childhood in the 1920s*
Stella Ashton; *80 pages, pen & ink drawings, £3.95*

WINIFRED: *Her Childhood and early working life*
Sylvia Marlow; *128 pages; Illustrated throughout; Price £4.50*

The **ROMANY WAY**
Irene Soper; *112 pages; Fully Illustrated; Price £4.95*

LAND GIRL: *Her Story of six years in the Women's Land*
Army, 1940-46 by Anne Hall
144 pages; Illustrated throughout; Price £4.95

LUMBER JILL:
Her Story of four years in the Women's Timber Corps
Mavis Williams; *96 pages; Illustrated; Price £3.95*

Ex Libris Press books may be obtained through your local book-
shop or direct from the publisher, post-free, on receipt of net price,
at: 1 The Shambles, Bradford on Avon, Wiltshire, BA15 1JS.
Please ask for our free, illustrated catalogue of around 50 titles.